BOOK 1 2 3 4

PANCHATANTRA

Author : Yogesh Joshi

Adaptation : Asmita Bhatt

1. THE FOX AND THE DRUM

There lived a fox in a forest. One day, he was roaming in the forest in search of food. Suddenly, he heard loud sounds...

BANG... BANG... BANG...

The fox was frightened. "What a deafening sound this is!" he thought. "It echoes through the forest! It seems to be the sound of some strange new animal. Let me run away from here."

But then he changed his mind. He thought, "If I run away, I might starve to death. Let me hide myself and see how big the animal is. If it lives by killing and eating other animals, it might share its prey with me."

The fox quietly walked in the direction from where the sound was coming. And what did he see? There was a big drum under a tree. The hanging branches of the tree were swaying in the breeze. As they swayed, they would strike against the drum; and this produced the sound of beats – BANG... BANG... BANG...

The drum might have been used by soldiers during a battle and since then, it must have been lying in that place. The fox hid himself behind a tree and watched the drum. He thought, "It is dangerous to be in this place. If this huge animal sees me, it will surely kill me and eat me up. Now I must leave this forest and go away."

But then the fox again thought, "This forest is my home. Why should I leave my home and go away? My mother used to say, 'Never make a hasty decision when you are frightened.' Let me go near the animal and observe it closely."

Although frightened, the fox slowly went near the drum. He said to himself, "As soon as this animal raises its paws to pounce on me, I will run away from here." But the animal did no such thing! So the fox went a little closer. But still the animal did not do anything. Now the fox gathered some courage. "Let me touch it," he thought and raised his paws and gently tapped on the drum.

BANG... The sound of the drum beat echoed through the forest.

The fox moved back a few steps. He again gathered courage and went closer to the drum. Now he was no longer frightened of the drum. He smelled it and thought, "How big this animal is! And, how thick its skin is! It must be very fleshy." The fox's mouth started watering.

The fox climbed up on the drum and tried to bite it. But the hide was too thick for the fox to bite into. He was surprised. "Such a big animal and yet it is so helpless! It cannot even face my attack. Poor animal!" said the fox to himself. The fox tried very hard to bite off a piece of the thick hide. But he broke his tooth instead! Blood began to drip from his mouth. The fox was very angry. Now with all his might, he bit into the hide. And, at last, he succeeded! Then it became very easy for him to tear it up. The fox was amazed. "I have bitten into this animal's skin and torn it open. And yet there is no blood," he wondered.

The fox entered the drum. It was hollow!

The fox sighed. He was disappointed.
He did not get any food to eat and, to add to his miseries, he had lost a tooth!

As the breeze blew, the branches of the tree struck against the drum. But this time, there were no sounds of the beats.

The fox said to himself, “Well, I don’t mind losing a tooth. But I am happy that I have lost my fright. I have killed this big animal.” The fox was very proud of himself.

The proud fox held his head high and, once again, began to wander in search of food.

2. THE LITTLE SANDPIPER AND HUGE SEA

A pair of sandpipers lived on a seashore. When it was time for Mother sandpiper to lay eggs, she said, "Find a nice safe place for me to lay eggs."

Father sandpiper said, "This seashore is so beautiful. Lay eggs here."

Mother sandpiper said, "No. This place is not safe. When the high tidal waves lash the shore, the sea will carry our eggs away. So you must find some other place for me."

Father sandpiper laughed and said, "How dare the sea carry our eggs away? You may lay eggs here without worrying about anything."

Hearing these words, the sea thought, "Ah! Look how proud this little bird is. What can he do if I carry away his eggs?"

Mother sandpiper laid eggs on the seashore.

One day, Mother sandpiper went in search of food. When she returned, she saw that her eggs had disappeared! The high tidal waves of the sea had carried the eggs away.

Mother sandpiper gave a shrill cry.

Tw...eet Tw...eet Tw...eet.

She could not stop lamenting.

When Father sandpiper came there, she said to him, "Didn't I tell you that the high tidal waves of the sea will carry our eggs away? I had advised you to find a safe place. But you did not heed my advice and look what has happened. Bring my eggs back to me."

Father sandpiper said, "Do not worry. I will not rest until I have brought the eggs back. I will dry up this cruel sea. I will drink all the waters of the sea with my beak."

Mother sandpiper said, “Have you gone mad? How can you drink the waters of the sea with your tiny beak? Yet if you wish to make enemies with the sea, you must take the help of all the other birds.”

Father sandpiper liked the suggestion. He called all the birds and narrated his tragic tale to them. He asked them to think of a way to empty the sea.

The birds discussed the problem among themselves and said, "We do not possess the power to empty the sea. Therefore, there is no point in trying to make an effort to do so. Yet let us go to our king, the eagle."

All the birds got together and went to the eagle. They began to lament saying, "The sea has carried away the eggs of these good-hearted sandpipers. The high tidal waves may destroy many others. You are our king. Please help us."

The eagle was grief-stricken to hear the story. He burst into a rage and said, "I can understand your grief. I will go right now and suck up the waters of the sea."

As the eagle was saying this, a messenger of Lord Vishnu came there and said, "O eagle! The Lord wants to go to Amaravati. He has called you at once."

Hearing this, the eagle said, "Convey my salutations to the Lord and please tell him to use someone else as his vehicle."

The messenger was astonished. He said, "Why do you say so? You have never been angry with the Lord. Why are you so angry today?"

The eagle said, "The sea is the abode of the Lord. The sea has carried away the eggs of our dear sandpipers. So please tell the Lord that he should leave the sea or else I refuse to serve him."

The messenger went to the Lord and gave the eagle's message to him. Hearing the message, Lord Vishnu Himself came to meet the eagle.

"Oh! The Lord himself is here to meet me," thought the eagle and he hung his head in shame.

He bowed to the Lord and said, "O Lord! The sea has carried away the eggs of the sandpipers. But I cannot dry up its waters because it is your abode."

The Lord said, "You are right. Come with me. We will get the eggs back from the sea. We will duly honour the sandpipers and then go to Amaravati."

The Lord went to the sea. He aimed the *Aagneyastra* at it and said, "O cruel sea! If you do not return the sandpipers' eggs to them, I will dry you up."

The sea was frightened.

It returned the sandpipers' eggs.

Mother sandpiper was very delighted.

She began to sing with joy.

Tw...eet Tw...eet Tw...eet.

3. THE THIEF AND THE GHOST

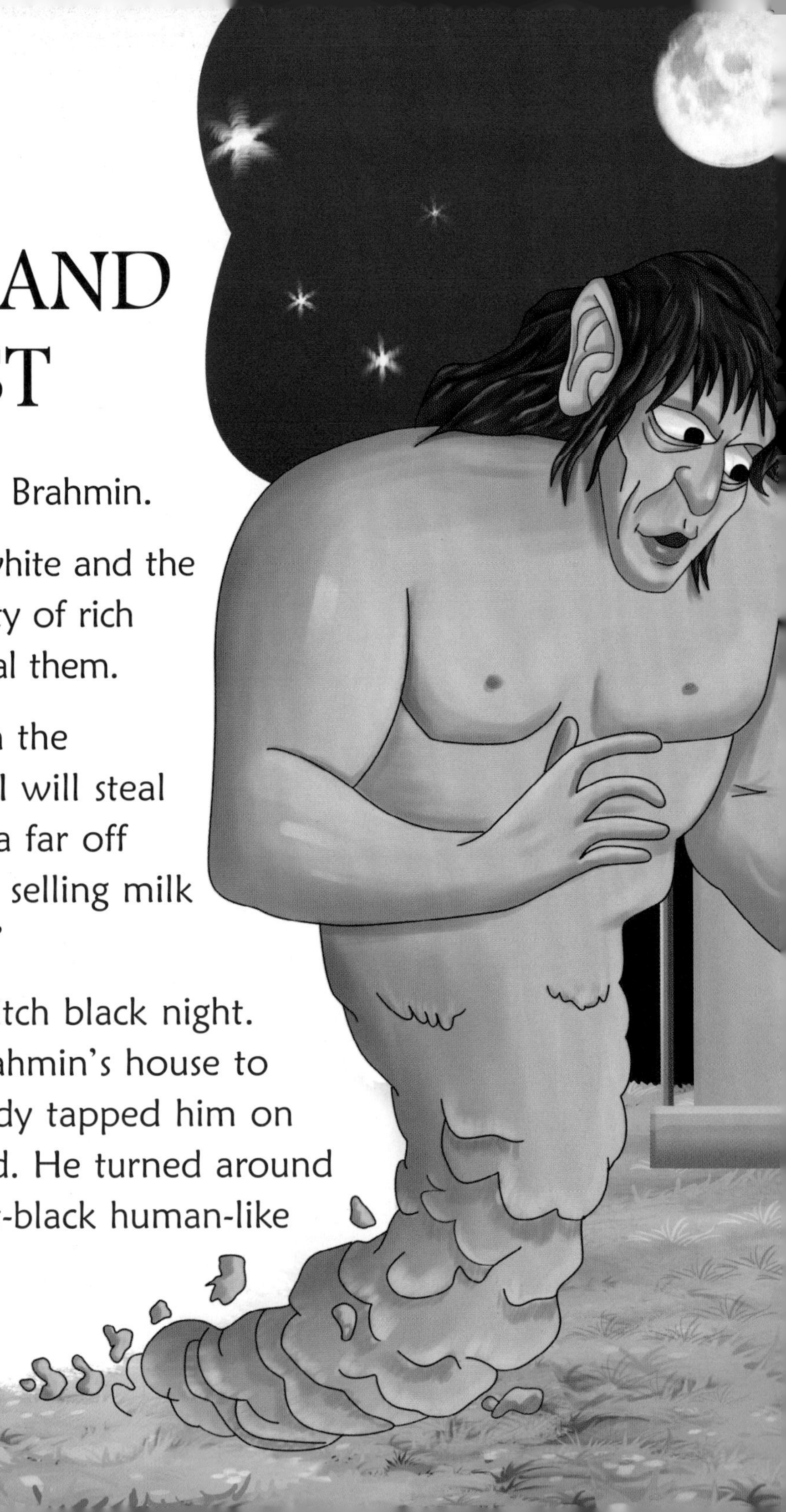

Once upon a time, there lived a Brahmin.

He had two cows–one was white and the other brown. Both cows gave plenty of rich milk. So a thief was tempted to steal them.

The thief thought, "Tonight, when the Brahmin household is fast asleep, I will steal the cows. I will then go away to a far off village and earn my livelihood by selling milk there. I won't have to steal then."

It was about midnight. It was a pitch black night. The thief tiptoed down to the Brahmin's house to steal the cows. Suddenly, somebody tapped him on his shoulder. The thief was startled. He turned around and what did he see?! A huge, jet-black human-like figure stood before him.

The thief said, "Who are you?"

"I am a ghost," said the figure, truthfully. "Who are you?"

"I am a thief," said the thief, frankly.

The ghost said to the thief, "Where do you intend to steal tonight?"

Pointing to the Brahmin's backyard, the thief said, "Tonight, I will steal the Brahmin's cows."

"And I intend to take the Brahmin away," said the ghost.

The thief and the ghost came to the Brahmin's house. They hid themselves and waited for the Brahmin family to retire.

The thief and the ghost waited till the lamp in the house was put out. The thief walked to the closed window and stood there for some time to make sure everyone was asleep. "I can hear the Brahmin snoring," he said in a whisper. "Wait here, while I go and steal the cows. Then you can take the Brahmin away."

The ghost said, "While you are stealing the cows, one of them may moo loudly and wake up the Brahmin. Therefore, I have a suggestion. Let me take the Brahmin away first. You can then steal the cows easily."

"No," said the thief. "I will go first."

"No," said the ghost. "It's my turn first."

Both were annoyed with each other. They were so angry that they did not realize what they were saying or doing.

The thief shouted saying, "Hey Brahmin... Wake up! Quickly! This ghost has come to take you away."

The ghost, too, shouted saying, "Wake up O Brahmin! This thief is here to steal your cows."

The Brahmin's son was awakened by the noise outside. He began to cry. The Brahmin lit the lamp.

The thief and the ghost ran away and soon they disappeared into the dark.

4. THE FOX AND THE SHEEP

One day, a fox was very hungry. He wandered and wandered, but he could not find any food to eat. He was very tired and he could hardly walk. With great difficulty, he reached the outskirts of a village.

Suddenly, the fox noticed two sheep fighting with each other. Now who would not like to witness a fight? The fox went a little closer to enjoy watching the fight between the two sheep. It appeared to be a fight to the finish.

Both sheep would strike their heads violently against each other's. They would then retreat a few steps, only to rush forward and again strike their heads violently.

The fox was enjoying himself. He thought, "If these two sheep keep on fighting in this manner, one of them is sure to die soon. And I will get enough food to satisfy my hunger."

As the fox was thinking this, the two sheep again struck their heads against each other's. Both began to bleed. The fox got the fine smell of fresh blood. His mouth started watering.

Now the two sheep were fighting even more violently. Blood began to trickle down their heads and the ground was covered with drops of fresh blood.

The fox was tempted to lick the fresh blood.

The fox went closer to the spot where the two sheep were fighting. He looked at the blood trickling down onto the ground. "What a waste of fresh blood!" thought the fox. "Let me lick it up quickly... slurp... slurp..."

Once again, the two sheep struck their heads against each other's. As they retreated a few steps to strike again, the fox dashed to the spot, licked some blood and returned to his place hastily.

The sheep struck their heads against each other's again. Some more blood trickled down onto the ground. And again, the fox rushed to that spot and licked the blood with a slurp. But before he could return to his place, the two sheep rushed forward and struck against his head.

The fox began to feel dizzy. He fell down on the ground and died.

The two sheep calmed down. They looked at the dead fox for some time and then walked away quietly.

5. IF I HAD DISOBEYED?

There lived a Brahmin in a small town.

One day, he had to go to some other town. As he was about to set out on his journey, his mother said, "Son, why are you going alone? You should take someone along with you."

The Brahmin said, "I have to cross the forest. But it is not dangerous as there are no wild animals or dacoits in the forest."

"But it is always better to have company," said the mother.

"Do not worry, mother," said the Brahmin. "Do not be afraid. I will go alone, complete my work and return home by tomorrow evening."

The mother went to the well in the backyard and came back with a crab in her hands. Giving it to her son, she said, "I don't think you should go alone. Here, take this crab with you."

The Brahmin took the crab, only to satisfy his mother. He put the crab in a bag along with some pieces of camphor. He then left hurriedly, carrying the bag on his shoulder.

It was a hot summer afternoon and the heat was unbearable. The Brahmin saw a big shady tree. "Let me rest under the tree for some time," he thought. "I will continue my journey after the heat has decreased."

Thinking this, the Brahmin sat under the tree and relished his lunch. He then lay down in the cool shade of the tree. Being tired, he soon dozed off.

Now it so happened that a snake lived in the hollow of the tree trunk. When it came out of the hollow, it saw the Brahmin fast asleep. The snake spotted the bag. It could get the smell of camphor coming from the bag. The snake loved the smell of camphor and so it slithered towards the bag. It slid into the bag and began to eat the pieces of camphor. The crab was roused and it came out of the bag. It held the snake firmly with its claws and began to suck its blood. The snake died.

The Brahmin woke up. He yawned and stretched. He then saw the dead snake on the pieces of camphor!

The Brahmin thanked God for saving his life. "The crab saved my life," he thought. "One should always obey one's mother. What would have happened if I had disobeyed mother?"

6. THE LION AND THE BULLOCK

Once upon a time, there lived a merchant.

One day, he loaded his goods in his bullock-cart, and accompanied by his servants, he left for Mathura. On his way, he had to cross a forest. As they reached the banks of a river, a bullock's leg got stuck in the mud. The bullock fell down and broke his leg.

The merchant loved the bullock very much. So he decided to stop there. But a servant said to him, "This forest is full of wild animals. For the sake of one bullock, it is not right to put everyone's life in danger."

The merchant agreed. He asked two of his servants to stay behind with the bullock to look after him. He then proceeded on his journey. The two servants were too scared to stay behind in the forest. So they left the bullock there and hurried to catch up with the merchant. They lied to the merchant saying, "The bullock is dead. We have come here after burying him."

But the bullock had a long life to live. Now he could eat the fresh, soft green grass growing on the banks of the river. After a few days, the bullock regained his health and became strong and plump–just like Lord Shiva's Nandi. He enjoyed his life on the banks of the river. He would strike his horns against the rocks and spend his time playing and bellowing loudly.

A lion lived in that forest. He was the king of the forest. One day, he was going to the river to drink water. Suddenly, he heard the bull's deafening bellow. The lion was frightened. The king of the forest ran and hid himself behind a tree!

A fox saw the frightened lion hiding behind the tree. He would follow the lion wherever he went, with the hope that the lion would appoint him as his minister. But when he saw that the lion was frightened, he thought, "This is a good opportunity. I must find out why the thirsty lion returned without drinking water from the river."

The fox went to the lion and bowed to him.

The lion raised his paws to bless the fox and then said, “Welcome. You are my old minister’s son. Tell me, what brings you here?”

The fox said, “Your Majesty! I do not want anything from you. I have come here only to assure myself about your well-being. But today, you look worried. Is anything bothering you? Are you in trouble?”

Suddenly, they heard the bullock’s ear-splitting bellow.

The lion said, “Did you hear that thunderous cry? Can you imagine how strong this animal must be? If this animal is stronger than I am, I do not wish to live in the forest.”

The fox said, "If you leave the forest and go away, what will happen to us? If you permit me, I will go and find out everything about this animal with a thunderous cry."

The lion gave his permission.

When the fox saw that the animal with the thunderous cry was only a harmless bullock, he was excited.

The fox went to the lion and said, "Your Majesty! I have found out everything about that animal with a thunderous cry. It is a very strong animal. But if you allow me, I will make him your humble servant."

The lion readily agreed. "In that case, I will make you my minister," he said happily.

The fox was only waiting for this opportunity. He went to the bullock. "Hey you bullock!" said the fox boastfully. "Why do you bellow so often? You are disturbing the lion's peaceful sleep. He is very angry with you and wants to see you at once."

The bullock shuddered with fright. He said to the fox, "You are a clever animal. Do what you must, but please request the lion to grant me the promise of safety."

The fox said, "Wait here. When the time comes, I will take you to the king."

The fox then went to the lion and said, "Your Majesty! This is no ordinary animal. He is Lord Shiva's Nandi himself."

The lion was even more frightened. The fox said, "I told him that the lion is the king of the forest and that he was the king's guest and so he should dine and enjoy with the king."

The lion was pleased. "Well done, fox," he said. "But please request him to grant me the promise of safety and bring him here with due honour."

Thus, the lion and the bullock became friends. The lion appointed the fox as his minister. Now the fox got a share of the lion's prey.

As the days passed, the lion and the bullock became good friends. Living with the bullock, the lion began to eat whatever the bullock ate. Soon he stopped killing animals and eating them up. And so, the fox also stopped getting his share of the lion's food.

"I will starve to death because of the friendship between the lion and the bullock," thought the fox. "Now I must think of a way to break their friendship. Tomorrow I will eat this bullock's flesh."

After thinking for some time, the fox went to the lion and said, "Your Majesty! I have to tell you a secret. I know you will not believe it."

"What is that?" asked the lion.

"The bullock told me that he knew how strong you are," said the fox. "He also told me that he would kill you tomorrow and declare himself the king of the forest."

The lion said, "I don't believe you. Do you have any proof?"

The fox said, "Didn't I tell you that you will not believe me? But wait till tomorrow morning. Tomorrow, you will see him burning with rage. His lips will quiver, and his bloodshot eyes will frighten you. Instead of sitting near you, he will sit far away – only to attack you."

The lion said, "Even if what you say is the truth, what can I do? I have promised him safety. How can I kill him?"

The fox said, "If he is planning to kill you and become the king, he does not deserve the promise of safety. If you do not kill him, he will surely kill you."

The fox then went to the bullock and said, "Somebody is poisoning the lion's mind against you. The lion is very angry with you. He has told me that tomorrow morning, he will kill you. How can a strong animal like the lion be a bullock's friend? Friend, I have come to warn you."

The bullock was frightened. He was so anxious that he could not sleep that night. He thought, "If the lion is angry with me, I will try to appease him and make him happy. Besides, the fox has already warned me not to sit near the lion. I will try to read the expressions on his face. If it becomes necessary, I will run away to save my life."

The next morning, the bullock went to the lion. He was so frightened that he did not have the courage to sit near the lion. His lips were quivering with fright. Since he had not slept all night, his eyes were red.

When the lion looked at the bullock, he remembered the fox's words. "The fox was telling me the truth," he thought. "As he had told me, the bullock is sitting at a distance. He is burning with rage and his eyes are bloodshot. Before he makes his next move, let me attack him."

At once the lion pounced on the bullock. The bullock did not get any time to run away. He had to struggle and fight against the mighty lion to save his own life. After a long fight, the bullock fell down dead.

7. THE FARMER AND THE SERPENT

There once lived a poor farmer in a small village.

The village had been affected by drought for three years. The farmer's land had dried up.

The winter had set in. One chilly evening, the farmer was resting under a tree in his land. As he looked around, he saw a serpent sitting by a burrow.

"The serpent lives here," thought the farmer. "But I have never worshipped it. That is why my land has dried up during the drought. Henceforth, I will worship the serpent regularly."

The farmer ran home and brought some milk. He placed the vessel of milk in front of the burrow and said, "O serpent! I did not know that you live here. Therefore I did not worship you. Please forgive me. But now I promise to worship you every day."

Saying this, the farmer offered milk to the serpent and went home. When he returned to his land the next morning, he saw something shining in the vessel! When he went a little closer, he saw a gold coin in the vessel!

From that day, every day, the farmer would offer milk to the serpent and get a gold coin in return!

One day, the farmer had to go to another village for some work. He asked his son to offer milk to the serpent every day.

That evening, the son went to the serpent to offer some milk. When he returned there the next morning, he saw a gold coin in the vessel!

The son thought, "This serpent is very stingy. I am sure there are countless gold coins in its burrow. Yet it gives only one gold coin every day. If I kill this serpent, I will get all the gold coins at once."

The next day, when the son went to offer milk to the serpent, he hit it on its head with a stick. The serpent was furious. It bit the farmer's son and killed him.

The serpent, too, was injured badly on its head. Writhing in pain, it slithered slowly into its burrow.

The farmer's relatives performed the funeral rites of the farmer's son.

When the farmer returned home, he was shocked to hear about the death of his son. He was angry with the serpent. But when the serpent told him what had actually happened, the farmer said, "O serpent! I know it was my son's fault. I apologize on his behalf."

The farmer then offered some milk to the serpent and again said, "Please forgive my son."

The serpent said, "Look at the funeral pyre of your son and look at my injured head. It was neither your son's fault nor mine. What has happened was inevitable. We are helpless against fate."

8. THE GOLDEN BIRD!

There was a beautiful forest, full of lush green trees.

One day, a hunter was passing through the forest. Suddenly, a bird sitting on a branch of a tree shed its droppings, which fell on the hunter's shoulder. The hunter looked at the droppings. There was gold in them!

The hunter was surprised. "I have been catching birds since my childhood," thought the hunter. "I am fifty now. But I have never seen gold in a bird's droppings."

The hunter looked up at the branch on which the bird was sitting. He was even more surprised! It was a golden bird! Once again the bird shed its droppings. And once again the hunter found that there was real gold in them!

The hunter cast his net and caught the golden bird, and took it home.

"At last... I will not have to go to the forest and catch birds to earn my living," thought the hunter, who was rather pleased. "I can easily get gold at home. I will sell the gold and earn my living. I need not worry at all now."

"But what if someone wants to know from where I get the gold?" wondered the hunter. "And if the king comes to know the secret, he will surely send me to the gallows. He may get angry with me for not presenting this unique and wonderful bird to him. Let me go and give this golden bird to the king."

The hunter took the cage and went to the king. He narrated his story to him. The king was delighted. "Give the best food to this bird and see to it that it is treated well," commanded the king to his attendants.

At once the Chief Minister said, "How can there ever be gold in a bird's droppings? This hunter has gone mad. Therefore, I request you to free the bird."

The king agreed with the Chief Minister.

The hunter opened the cage.

The golden bird flew out and sat on a pillar in the court.

It then shed its droppings. And, gold was shining brightly in them!

Everyone present there was astonished.

Suddenly, the golden bird said in human voice, "I am the first fool, because I shed my droppings on the hunter's shoulder.

The second fool is the hunter. In spite of catching me, he could not keep me.

The third fool is the Chief Minister. He advised the king to free me even before making sure whether I shed droppings with gold in them.

The fourth fool is the king. Why did he heed the Chief Minister's advice?"

Having said this, the bird lapped its wings and flew away.